How to Hear from God

Personal Study Guide

D0113570

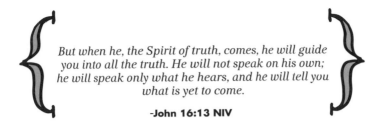

But when he, the Spirit of truth, comes, he will guide you into all the truth. He will not speak on his own; he will speak only what he hears, and he will tell you what is yet to come.

-John 16:13 NIV

Many people have a hard time believing God wants to speak to them. They think that although He spoke directly to people in the Bible, He doesn't do that today. But God still speaks today—and He wants to speak to you.

The truth is, if you're going to really experience a personal relationship with Him, you need to know how to hear His voice.

The purpose of this study guide is to help you take the teachings from the *How to Hear from God* book and CDs and practically apply the biblical principles about communicating with God.

As you read each of the four sections, you'll discover how to go deeper in your personal relationship with Him. You will gain a stronger confidence that God really does want to speak to you, discover the many ways He communicates with you, experience the benefits of obeying His voice, and know how to set the right atmosphere so it's easier to hear from Him.

My prayer is that you'll begin hearing from God on a far greater level than you ever thought possible. And I believe that as you do, your life will never be the same!

Love,

Joyce

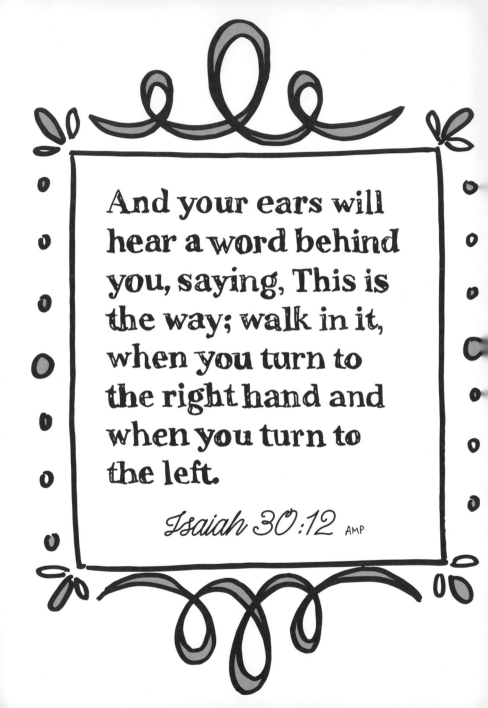

And your ears will
hear a word behind
you, saying, This is
the way; walk in it,
when you turn to
the right hand and
when you turn to
the left.

Isaiah 30:12 AMP

You Can—
And Need to—
Hear from God

YOU CAN HEAR FROM GOD

The truth is, you can hear from God. In fact, you are designed to hear God's voice because He desires a personal relationship with you. When you accepted Christ as your Savior and began a one-on-one relationship with Him, the Holy Spirit came to live in you. Through Him, you live in God's presence 24/7.

> *But the Comforter (Counselor, Helper, Intercessor, Advocate, Strengthener, Standby), the Holy Spirit, Whom the Father will send in My name [in My place, to represent Me and act on My behalf], He will teach you all things. And He will cause you to recall (will remind you of, bring to your remembrance) everything I have told you.*
>
> **John 14:26**

What does this scripture tell you about who the Holy Spirit

is and how He wants to help you, or work, in your life?

> *But when He, the Spirit of Truth (the Truth-giving Spirit) comes, He will guide you into all the Truth (the whole, full Truth). For He will not speak His own message [on His own authority]; but He will tell whatever He hears [from the Father; He will give the message that has been given to Him], and He will announce and declare to you the things that are to come [that will happen in the future].*
>
> **John 16:13**

According to John 16:13, what does the Holy Spirit reveal to you? Where does His direction come from and how does He share it with you?

YOU NEED TO HEAR FROM GOD

> *I can of Myself do nothing. As I hear, I judge; and My judgment is righteous, because I do not seek My own will but the will of the Father who sent Me.*
>
> **John 5:30 NKJV**

Knowing you can hear from God is the first step, but recognizing that you have a need to hear from God in order to be able to handle everything that happens each day is another matter entirely. Jesus, our example of how we should live, shows us why we need to hear God's voice and how to do it in John 5:30.

Study this verse and note what you discover about this.

(Check out John 15:5 to take this even deeper.)

21 Days Fix   30 min
Eating plan   3x
1800 ~~——~~ 6290
~~——~~ 530 —   19,95

It's human nature for us to want to make our own decisions apart from God, especially if we don't understand that we *can* and *need* to hear His voice. Our emotions want to tell us how to feel about everything, and it's common for our will to contradict and even rebel against God's will. Even Jesus had to make a choice to do only God's will instead of living every day completely independent to follow His own desires.

Be willing to hear from God about everything, not just during the times when you are desperate, in trouble, or when you need an answer about something that is really important to you. Living this way will not only strengthen your relationship with God, but will save you a great deal of unnecessary suffering, frustration and exhaustion in the long run.

The bottom line is, if you want to hear from God, you must be willing to do what He says. And remember: Everything God tells us to do is for our good.

Read Philippians 1:9-10 What is it that causes us to grow in knowledge and understanding of God's will so we can hear His voice more clearly and consistently? How do you plan to apply this to your life this week?

_____

_____

_____

_____

_____

_____

Read Jeremiah 6:10 and 2 Chronicles 7:14. According to these scriptures, what must we do to hear God's voice?

_____

_____

_____

_____

_____

_____

_____

_____

_____

Read 1 Corinthians 2:9-11. What does this scripture tell you about the Holy Spirit's relationship to the Father, and how can this help you every day?

_____

_____

_____

_____

_____

_____

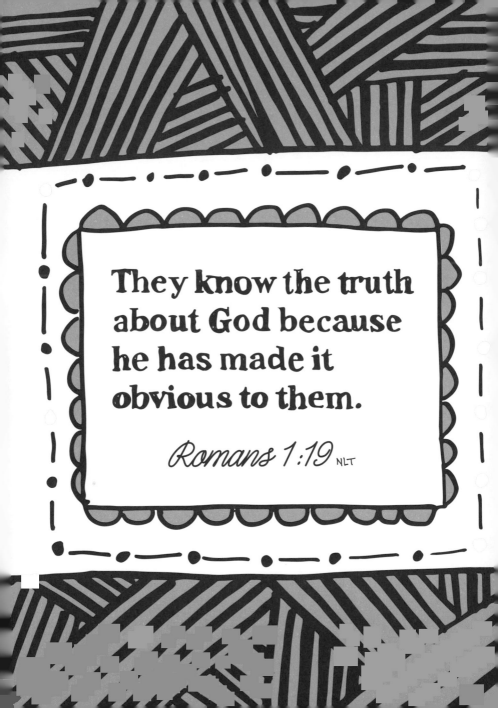

They know the truth about God because he has made it obvious to them.

Romans 1:19 NLT

How God Speaks to You

> *"God speaks to us in many different ways, so we have to be careful not to get our minds made up about **how** we want to hear from Him."*
>
> **-Joyce**

God wants to speak to you continually—every day. Discerning God's voice is not something you will automatically know how to do. It's something we learn how to do as we spend quality time with God, growing in our faith and getting closer to Him. It takes practical experience, understanding and wisdom to know if what you're hearing, thinking or sensing is really from God.

While there are many ways to hear from God, this section will explore seven of the most common ways God speaks.

1. GOD'S WORD

So Jesus said to those Jews who had believed in Him, If you abide in My word [hold fast to My teachings and live in accordance with them], you are truly My disciples. And you will know the Truth, and the Truth will set you free.

John 8:31-32

The Bible is one of the most common ways God speaks to you. God's Word is His practical wisdom that reveals life-changing truth. It gives you understanding, teaches you, and builds your hope. The Bible is our instruction book for life!

John 1:1 says, *In the beginning [before all time] was the Word (Christ), and the Word was with God, and the Word was God Himself.*

The Word gives you God's perspective, exposes wrong thinking and protects you. God's Word reveals His will in contrast to your own thoughts and desires. If you really want to hear God's voice, you need to be a student of God's Word.

How is God speaking to you through His Word? Consider all the

ways you have read or heard God's Word. Has the Word ever

been an answer to a problem or an encouragement you needed?

2. NATURE

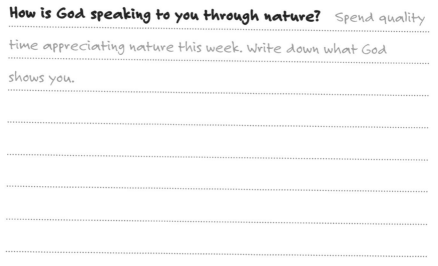

The heavens declare the glory of God; and the firmament shows and proclaims His handiwork.

Psalm 19:1

It's important to pay attention to the beauty of nature because it reminds you that no matter what is happening in your life, God is bigger—He is more than able to help and take care of you, no matter what you are going through.

God speaks through everything He has made.

Romans 1:20 (NLT) says, *For ever since the world was created, people have seen the earth and sky. Through everything God made, they can clearly see his invisible qualities—his eternal power and divine nature…*

Take time to appreciate nature. Spend time outdoors walking or hiking… consider the calming affect that comes from watching a sunrise or sunset, or listening to birds, ocean waves, or a gentle wind blowing through trees. These experiences sharpen your senses and make it easier for you to draw near to God's heart.

How is God speaking to you through nature? Spend quality

time appreciating nature this week. Write down what God

shows you.

3. CONVENTIONAL WISDOM AND COMMON SENSE

 If any of you is deficient in wisdom, let him ask of the giving God [Who gives] to everyone liberally and ungrudgingly, without reproaching or faultfinding, and it will be given him.
James 1:5

Have you ever seen someone who is intellectually smart but makes a lot of bad choices? This is because common sense and wisdom are not gained through textbooks, but from challenging life experiences, a relationship with God, and time spent in His Word.

Sometimes we know how to handle situations simply by using conventional wisdom and common sense. Wisdom discerns truth in a situation, while common sense provides good judgment about what to do with the truth.

How is God speaking to you through conventional wisdom and common sense? Can you remember a time when God prompted you to use wisdom and common sense? Or maybe you're facing a situation right now and need to rely on them for direction.

4. DREAMS AND VISIONS

"In the last days, God says, I will pour out my Spirit on all people. Your sons and daughters will prophesy, your young men will see visions, your old men will dream dreams. Even on my servants, both men and women, I will pour out my Spirit in those days, and they will prophesy."

Acts 2:17-18 NIV

We live in an era that the Bible refers to as "the last days," and while dreams and visions are not necessarily the most typical way to hear from God, we see in His Word that they are ways He sometimes chooses to speak to us.

God uses dreams to tell us of things that are going to happen in the future, to warn us about something that's coming so we are prepared, or to get our attention when we wrestle with Him about something He's trying to deal with us about.

A vision from God will cause you to have a deep understanding within your spirit that what you've seen will come to pass. It will strengthen your faith in ways that compel you to want to see it through.

Is God speaking to you through dreams and visions? Has

God ever given you a dream or a vision? If so, write it down. This

will help you focus on God's promise while He guides you, bringing

it to pass in His perfect timing.

5. PROPHESY

 ...The one who prophesies [who interprets the divine will and purpose in inspired preaching and teaching] speaks to men for their upbuilding and constructive spiritual progress and encouragement and consolation.

1 Corinthians 14:3

"Prophesy" is a message God speaks through other people to reveal His will for your life. In the body of Christ, there are people who prophesy (Acts 2:18) to edify and build people up, and there are those who stand in the office of a prophet, who usually have stronger words for the church. Both are very important gifts of the Holy Spirit.

Sometimes, a prophetic word will confirm what is already in your heart. Other times, someone may prophesy something over you that you never considered before. When that happens, write down what you heard and set it aside—much like placing it on a "shelf" in your mind. Then pray for God's will and understanding as you wait on His timing. It could be years later before something suddenly happens that makes you think, *Wait a minute...what is this?* And the Holy Spirit will remind you of that prophetic word you received long ago.

That said, use caution to avoid replacing God's Word with prophesies as your preferred method for hearing from God. Rather than chase after prophetic gifts, allow God to decide how and when to speak to you.

Has God spoken to you through prophesy? Has someone ever told you something that you knew was from God? Was it a confirmation of something you believed in your heart or an encouraging word to take a step of faith? How did you respond?

6. SANCTIFIED DESIRES

For the desires of the flesh are opposed to the [Holy] Spirit, and the [desires of the] Spirit are opposed to the flesh (godless human nature); for these are antagonistic to each other [continually withstanding and in conflict with each other], so that you are not free but are prevented from doing what you desire to do.

Galatians 5:17

Another way God may speak to you is through desire—*sanctified* desire. This happens when God places His desires in your heart, which are different from your natural, fleshly desires. As you can see in Galatians 5:17, the Bible says the desires of the flesh are directly opposed to the desires of the Spirit.

Here's the difference: A natural—or carnal—desire will always torment you because you have no peace about it. But when a desire is from God, you have such a peace inside that you are not tormented by it.

A desire from God can become a burning desire—driving you internally to want to succeed. This kind of desire will motivate you to override whatever opposition comes your way. Then there are times when God may give you a simple desire—something He wants to bless you with—and He places it in your heart to encourage you to pray for it.

The best thing you can do is follow the wisdom of Psalm 37:4: *Delight yourself also in the Lord, and He will give you the desires and secret petitions of your heart.*

Is God speaking to you through the desires of your heart?

If you have a desire in your heart that you believe is from God,

be sure it lines up with His Word. Write your desire as a prayer to the Lord, and revisit it in a couple of weeks to see how He has responded to you.

7. THE "INNER WITNESS"

And let the peace (soul harmony which comes) from Christ rule (act as umpire continually) in your hearts [deciding and settling with finality all questions that arise in your minds, in that peaceful state] to which as [members of Christ's] one body you were also called [to live]. And be thankful (appreciative), [giving praise to God always].

Colossians 3:15

The most common way God speaks to you is through your "inner witness"—otherwise known as your conscience. When you sense *peace* through your inner witness, this is a confirmation that you are hearing from God.

Peace should be the umpire of your soul—deciding what's "safe" and what's "out." Simply put, if you don't feel right about it, don't do it. Sometimes you will know the reason why, and other times you will not. You don't always have to know the details when you don't feel at peace. Likewise, if someone doesn't agree with your decision, you don't have to justify yourself and can say, "I'm doing what I'm peaceful about doing."

Listening to your inner witness, or conscience, takes a lot of practice, and you are likely to make mistakes. It's part of the process of learning and growing spiritually. The thing to remember is that God is bigger than your mistakes and you can learn from them. And because you belong to God, He orders your steps (Psalm 37:23), and will ultimately work your mistakes out for good (Romans 8:28).

How is God speaking to you through your inner witness?

This week, be aware of a moment when you sense your inner

witness guiding you. Record your experience here, and explain

how you responded to it.

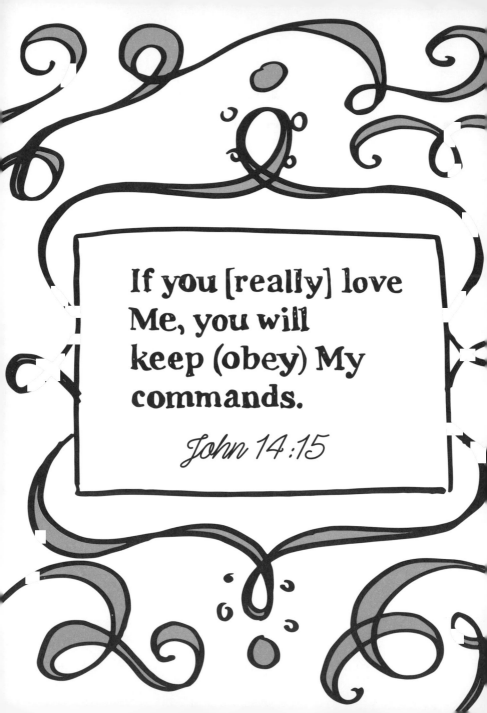

If you [really] love Me, you will keep (obey) My commands.

John 14:15

The Rewards of Obedience

> *"God doesn't want us to obey Him to buy His love. He wants us to obey Him because we trust Him... because we believe anything He asks us to do or not to do is for our good. God is a good God. Everything He asks us to do is for our good!"*
>
> **-Joyce**

God wants you to have the very best life that He can possibly give you. He loves you, and everything He tells you to do is for your good. He always has your best interest at heart, and living in obedience to His Word is the key to the most joyful, peaceful, fulfilling life you could ever experience.

We need to see obedience to God as the pathway to the good life we want to live. And when our obedience is a *lifestyle* we have more ability to hear God's voice.

Our motive for obeying God is vitally important. When you are willing to obey God in all things, you are demonstrating that you depend on Him for everything in your life, rather than living independently and only seeking God when you want something from Him.

Obedience that draws you closer to God is motivated by a heart of love for Him and a sincere desire to do what's right. As John 14:15 says, we show we really love God by obeying His direction for our lives.

Proverbs 1:23-30 helps us understand the importance of obedience to God, following His wisdom for our lives. What are the warnings He gives for disobedience?

BARRIERS TO HEARING FROM GOD

God wants to speak to us continually, but sometimes we can't hear Him because of barriers that keep us from receiving His voice. In her teaching, Joyce reveals specific issues or conditions that cause this problem and how obedience to God's way is the solution. Study the key scriptures that follow to see what they are and how you can overcome them.

I. Independent Attitudes

Jeremiah 10:23 and John 15:5 What do these scriptures reveal as a barrier to hearing God's voice and living in His will for your life?

Psalm 40:6 According to this scripture, what are the two things God has provided to you to eliminate this barrier?

II. Guilt

1 John 3:21 What causes this common emotion that hinders our sensitivity to God's voice?

Read **I John 1:9** and **Romans 8:1** to find the remedy.

....

....

....

....

....

....

....

III. Grumbling & Complaining

I Thessalonians 5:18 This verse is a major key to always

maintain a clear line of communication with God. What is it?

....

....

....

....

....

....

....

Study these additional scriptures for more insight into the power of an attitude of gratitude and ways you can develop it.

- **Psalm 34:1**

- **Philippians 2:14-15 and 4:6**

- **1 Corinthians 10:9-11**

- **Ephesians 5:18-20**

IV. Outside Influences

Proverbs 4:20-23 This passage is a valuable word of wisdom that can help you protect your heart from a particular road-block to intimacy with God. What barrier does it address and how does it help you avoid it?

....

....

....

....

....

....

....

Mark chapter 4 talks about the Parable of the Sower. **According to this passage, what does verse 19 have to do with someone's ability to hear from God?**

What do verses 23-25 tell you about what is required to hear from God?

Hebrews 5:7-11 What example did Jesus give us through His relationship with God, and what causes sluggishness and the inability to achieve spiritual insight?

What are ways you can make sure your mind stays sharp so you can hear clearly from God?

V. Doubt & Unbelief

Doubt, unbelief, and an unwillingness to trust God will not only hinder your ability to hear from God, they weaken—and can block—your ability to obey Him.

Genesis 17:1-2 When God called Abraham to "Go...away from your country," He gave him step one but not step two. What does Abraham's example in obeying God say to us about walking by faith?

Romans 4:18-20 According to this passage, how did Abraham grow stronger, and why did it happen?

Based on your previous response, what does this reveal about your ability to trust God with seemingly impossible situations?

BE TOTALLY DEPENDENT ON GOD

Everyone has things in their lives they want to overcome. This includes the stuff that you know you probably shouldn't be doing but are trying to work with God to overcome. That's where grace comes in—when God gives you ability and favor to accomplish what you need to do because He knows you are sincerely striving to obey Him and depend on Him for the strength to do it.

God has a part, and you have a part. God wants to bring His plan for your life to completion, but a lifestyle of obedience is key to making it all happen.

Isaiah 11:2 According to this scripture, what does the Spirit of the Lord provide to those who are obedient?

James 1:5-6 According to this passage, what does God do when you ask Him for wisdom?

What is required of those who ask God for help, and why is it important?

Let be and be still, and know (recognize and understand) that I am God. I will be exalted among the nations! I will be exalted in the earth!

Psalm 46:10

Creating an Atmosphere in Which God Will Speak

> *"An ATMOSPHERE is a climate, an environment, or a predominant mood that is in the room around you. Atmospheres are created by attitudes."*
>
> **-Joyce**

ATTITUDES DETERMINE ATMOSPHERES

In fact, the climate of your attitude is directly connected to your ability to hear clearly from God and not be distracted from what He wants to say or do. Hearing from God requires active listening, and active listening is something we choose to do on purpose, regardless of what is happening around us.

For example, if you want to make plans to be outdoors next weekend, you want to make sure the climate will be good. You turn on the news and wait for the weather report. You might do other things in the meantime, but you are actively tuning your ear toward that station so that, when the weather forecast is broadcasted, you will hear and pay attention to it.

Hearing from God requires a similar "listening ear." This takes a bit of practice and some adjustments in thought and behavior, because in order to be able to tune in and hear from God, you must first realize that He desires to be in communication and companionship with you constantly.

Consider that when you listen for something on purpose, you are ready to receive information at any moment. The same is true when we turn our ears toward God and make ourselves available to hear from Him at any time. If you don't believe you can hear from God or simply are not willing to listen, He probably won't speak.

There are many kinds of attitudes that influence atmospheres, but in this section, we will examine three major attitudes that can draw you closer to God so you can hear from Him clearly.

ATTITUDE #1: THE WISDOM OF KNOWING WHEN TO BE SILENT

> *But when God, who set me apart from my mother's womb and called me by his grace, was pleased to reveal his Son in me so that I might preach him among the Gentiles, my immediate response was not to consult any human being. I did not go up to Jerusalem to see those who were apostles before I was, but I went to Arabia. Later I returned to Damascus.*
> **Galatians 1:15-17 NIV**

The apostle Paul had enough wisdom to know that there are times when consulting other people about what God says is not the right thing to do, particularly when what He said requires a radical change in your life. Paul waited three years before approaching anyone about his encounter with Jesus, which was wise for him to do.

Likewise, there will be times when God reveals something to you that causes you to step way outside of your comfort zone. It could be something extraordinary or specific about your future. When this happens, it's important to use wisdom in order to honor what God said.

You may be tempted to ask for advice or seek encouragement from friends and family in your excitement. But if God isn't leading you to do that, it may confuse you because everyone will tell you something different, or they won't agree with you altogether.

Understand that God gives you the faith to take one step at a time toward the dream or desire He's placed in your heart. He will stretch your faith by pulling you so far outside of your comfort zone that you have to depend on Him alone to reach the fulfillment of it. And it's important to know when to remain silent and when it's okay to share it with someone else.

Think about this...

- What dreams and desires are in your heart that you believe God has given to you?

- Have you shared them with anyone? If you have, how did it affect your faith in God to make it happen?

- If you're feeling discouraged, confused or frustrated, take time to pray and ask God to help you be still so you can tune in to His voice alone and confidently hear what He's speaking to your heart.

ATTITUDE #2: KNOWING WHEN TO WAIT ON GOD

 *Blessed (happy, fortunate, to be envied) is the man who lis-
tens to me, watching daily at my gates, waiting at the posts
of my doors.*

Proverbs 8:34

There will be times when you think you are hearing from God, but you're actually responding to something out of your emotions. These situations can range from an amazing, once-in-a-lifetime opportunity to a sale at a favorite store.

Whenever this happens, wait and listen for God to guide you. Set your mind to want God's will more than you want anything else. You'll hear much quicker and more clearly from God if you refuse to act in the heat of emotion, and you're determined to do what God says—even if it hurts or costs you something.

The same holds true for new opportunities that require a commitment from you. You must be aware of what is expected so you can prepare yourself for the duration of that commitment. The fact is, the excitement of new opportunities will always wear off. Those emotions that initially energized you will fade, and when that happens, you'll have to set your mind to be a person of integrity by keeping your word and doing your best no matter how you feel. To do so, you will need God's grace and determination to follow through and finish what you committed to do.

You can also make matters worse if, when your emotions are stirred up, you rush into confronting or responding to someone or something without God's direction or timing to do so. This is another time when you need to take a break and wait on God.

Think about this...

- Is there any circumstance that has stirred up your emotions, tempting you to take an action that may not be led by God?

- "Wait to decide until your emotions subside" is a helpful rule of thumb when you aren't sure if you're being moved by feelings or what God is saying to you. How could you apply this to your life right now?

ATTITUDE #3: A WILLINGNESS TO PRAY AND OBEY

Sacrifice and offering You do not desire, nor have You delight in them; You have given me the capacity to hear and obey [Your law, a more valuable service than] burnt offerings and sin offerings [which] You do not require.

Psalm 40:6

God has given you the ability to hear and obey Him. Some things God says will excite you, but other times, you might not like what you hear. That's when obedience is key.

Some people only listen to God when it's comfortable to do so—when He tells them what they want to hear. But God knows what's best for you. He will never tell you to do something that is not good for you. He wants to be your Counselor, Protector, Comforter and Provider. He wants to prepare you to move forward in His plans for your life by stretching your faith and increasing your trust in Him. And for this to happen, there will be times when God asks you to do something that will cost you or even create hardships.

The bottom line is, the most valuable thing you can ever do is spend time with God in prayer and by studying His Word. And as He speaks to your heart, do whatever He tells you to do. The rewards of obedience will always outweigh the price we may pay to follow God!

Think about this...

- Is there any area of your life that God is directing you to make a change but you're struggling with it?

- Are you battling fear of giving up something you love...discouraged by past attempts to change that have failed...or just feeling frustrated that you have to deal with something God is telling you to do?

- Simply taking more time to pray and study Scripture about trusting God and obeying His voice will make the difference.

First Printing, 2015
ISBN 978-1-942854-03-6
Joyce Meyer Ministries, P.O. Box 655, Fenton, Missouri 63026
joycemeyer.org

THE HOLY BIBLE, NEW INTERNATIONAL VERSION®, NIV® Copyright © 1973, 1978, 1984, 2011 by Biblica, Inc.® Used by permission. All rights reserved worldwide.

Scripture quotations marked (NLT) are taken from the Holy Bible, New Living Translation, copyright © 1996, 2004, 2007 by Tyndale House Foundation. Used by permission of Tyndale House Publishers, Inc., Carol Stream, Illinois 60188. All rights reserved.

Scripture taken from the New King James Version®. Copyright © 1982 by Thomas Nelson. Used by permission. All rights reserved.